The publishers wish to acknowledge the kind assistance of Mr Michael Chinery in the preparation of this book.

© 1979, 1982 by Grisewood & Dempsey Ltd

Designed and produced by Grisewood & Dempsey Ltd,
Elsley Court, 20-22 Great Titchfield Street, London W1

Published in 1982 in this edition by Galley Press,
an imprint of W H Smith and Son Limited
Registered No 237811 England.
Trading as WHS Distributors, St John's House,
East Street, Leicester, LE1 6NE

ISBN 0 86136 955 6

Printed and bound in Portugal by Printer Portuguesa, Sintra.

The Duck

By Angela Sheehan
Illustrated by Maurice Pledger
and Bernard Robinson

Galley Press

Well out of the wind, with her head tucked under her feathers, the duck slept. Nearby in the water, several drakes dabbled for food. They stabbed the surface with their beaks, or up-ended themselves completely to catch the tiny water creatures. Most of the rest of the flock were pecking at the weeds on the edge of the lake.

When she woke, the duck preened her feathers, and then waddled down to the water.

As she swam the duck stretched out her neck and the drakes circled round her. Each male wanted the female to notice him. One thrust his bill into the water and shook a shower of water droplets; another jerked his head and bill up and down to show off his fine breast; one whistled and the others grunted.

The female seemed not to notice their displays. But she had seen them all. As she swam away, she turned her head and nodded to one of the drakes. He fluffed up his feathers and paddled after her, leaving the others to watch.

The duck and drake swam together every day from then on, and at night they flew to the same field to eat. They dug in the soil for worms and slugs, and pecked in the ditches to find the last of the acorns. But the weather was cold and there was not enough food for them, or the rest of the flock.

So one evening all the birds gathered on the water and took off together to fly south. The beating of their wings sounded like the whistling of a fierce wind. They flew all night. In the morning they stopped to feed and rest. The duck and drake pecked about in the hard soil and then slept until evening when they flew on again. By morning they had reached the coast. There they spent the second day, before continuing their journey.

As the sun dropped low in the sky, the ducks took off again, flying high above the waves. Soon they were over land again, but it was not time to rest. They flew on and on until the sun was high in the sky. Then they came upon a large, peaceful lake, where they could stop.

The lake was already the home of swans, geese, mallards like themselves, and many other kinds of ducks, but there was room for more. The duck and the drake closed their tired wings, tucked in their heads and fell asleep on the calm water.

When they woke, the two birds explored the lake, nibbling at the weeds that spread over its surface and poking about in the reeds. The grassy meadows beyond were full of good food, and the pair were soon too full to do anything but float.

Day after day, they swam together or flew off to find food. Even in the winter the duck and drake were able to find berries and nuts hidden in the woods, or scraps left out at the farm for the cats.

There was plenty to eat; it was harder for them to keep warm. When the edge of the lake froze, they left the water and huddled together under a hawthorn bush. Its tangle of thin branches did little to keep out the icy wind, or the snow and rain that drenched their feathers. And as well as bad weather, there were hungry enemies about. At night, a fox prowled by the lakeside and an otter slipped silently across the ice.

As soon as the weather grew warmer, the pair flew back to the lake they had left in the autumn. It was the lake where they had hatched the year before. Not all the flock returned home. Some stayed where they were or else stopped near the coast.

Spring was just beginning. The lake weeds were fresh and green, and the reedy banks were full of croaking frogs and buzzing insects. Each day the drake whistled to the duck, and showed off his feathers to her, for she would soon be ready to mate. There were still other males who wanted to mate with her but the drake drove them away. The duck was to be his, first.

After the two had mated, the drake stayed with the duck, and kept the other drakes away from her while she looked for a place to build her nest.

The duck found a dense clump of grass, deep inside a gorse hedge. When the bracken grew up, the mound would be completely hidden. The duck stamped on the grass to make it flatter. Then, she scraped out a hollow in the centre. In between trips to the water to dabble for food, she collected leaves, grasses and feathers to line the nest. On top of these she spread a layer of soft, downy feathers from her own breast.

A few nights later, exactly four weeks after
she had mated, the duck climbed on to the nest.
In a few hours she laid her first egg. Afterwards she
felt hungry. So she plucked some downy feathers
from her breast and spread them over the egg. On
top she put a layer of leaves to hide it. Then she
squeezed through the wall of plants and waddled
down to the water to feed.

The next day, she laid a second egg, and then
for eight days, she laid one egg a day. When all the
eggs were laid, she settled down to hatch them with
the help of her warm body. So long as she kept the
eggs warm, the ducklings inside the shells would
continue to grow. They had the egg yolks for food.

The duck fed herself early in the morning or at dusk. She never stayed away from the nest for long. And before she left she always covered the eggs with leaves. They must not cool or come to any harm.

She sometimes saw the drake when she went to feed. But now that she had eggs to tend, she had no time for him, so he went off to find another duck.

For a month, the duck sat alone and hidden on the eggs. Then one afternoon she heard a tapping sound from under her feathers. She peered down in time to see the shell of one of the eggs crack open. From the jagged opening came a tiny, wet head, all beak and eyes. Then all the other eggs began to crack, and before long the nest was a jumble of broken shells and chirping ducklings.

Gently, the duck cleared the bits of broken shell from round the ducklings' trembling bodies and waited for their light, fluffy feathers to dry. All the time, the bony little birds were stretching and struggling, and trying to clamber to the edge of the nest. When they were dry, the duck gave each one a gentle push over the edge of the nest. They tumbled down to the ground, one after the other.

The duck jumped out after the little birds.
and waited while they pushed themselves up on to
their big, flat feet. With feet as long as their legs,
it was difficult for them to walk. But now their
mother was waddling away and they had to follow
her. She went so fast it was all they could do to
keep up. They had no time to look about them and
see all the strange, new sights.

When they reached the lake, the duck eased herself into the water and the ducklings followed. Paddling was much easier than walking. They pushed the water with their big flappy feet and sailed along in a line behind their mother. Every now and then, she dipped her head into the water and up-ended her whole body. The ducklings tried to do the same but they were not old enough to dabble yet. They had to make do with snapping up insects on the surface of the water.

By the time their mother had eaten enough, the sun had almost sunk. The walk home was long, cold and windy. And the ducklings were so tired they had to be helped back into the nest. They snuggled up to their mother and fell fast asleep.

Each day their mother marched them down to the lake. The ducklings knew how to swim from the very start, but they still had to learn how to fly. Until they could fly, they would be in danger every time they left the nest. Even when they were swimming with their mother there were enemies.

One morning a pike with great curved teeth followed the family as they floated along. It watched the eleven pairs of feet paddling above, and waited. As soon as one of the ducklings up-ended itself, the fish pounced. The little duckling disappeared into its hungry stomach.

Another evening the brood were late to leave the water. An otter, which usually did not come out of its holt until after dusk, caught the ducks' scent as they passed. The creature surfaced just as the last and smallest duckling was struggling towards the bank, far behind the others. The tired little duckling was easy prey for the swift otter.

At almost the same moment, a marsh harrier swooped down from the sky and snatched another of the ducklings in its talons. The duck saw it coming and quacked loudly but she could not protect her brood. They must learn to fly and look after themselves.

But the ducklings' wings were not yet strong enough for flying; their feathers were too short. The little birds could only hop into the air and float gently down to the ground.

As the weeks passed, their wing muscles grew stronger and their feathers grew longer. At last they could flap their wings and take off. They skimmed across the surface of the lake and then lifted themselves high into the air. They perched in the tall trees and flew to faraway fields.

The duck watched her brood from the water, as they flew back and forth. They did not need her any longer and she could no longer care for them. She could not even fly herself now, for she had lost most of her wing feathers. The other ducks and drakes had moulted, too. The drakes looked more and more like ducks as their colourful feathers dropped out one by one. All the adults stayed out of sight as much as possible, for they were almost as helpless as ducklings without their flight feathers.

Late in the summer, the birds began to grow
new feathers. The ducklings were fully fledged now,
and the young males proudly displayed their new
flight feathers to their sisters. Their mother spent
her days preening her feathers and dabbling on the
lake. At night she often flew to her favourite field
to feed. She hardly ever saw the fine young birds
she had reared.

When autumn came, she found a new mate. The old drake did the same, and so did some of their brood. Soon they would all fly south to escape the bitter winter. Perhaps, in spring, the young ducks would return to the lake as their parents had done the year before. Then it would be their turn to bring up a brood of ducklings.

More About Ducks

topside
of drake

underside
of duck

strong wing
feathers for
flying

preen
gland

webbed feet
for paddling

**The mallard duck and
drake. The drake
(right) is about 58 cms
long. The duck is
slightly smaller but
her quack is louder.**

Where to see mallards

There are many different kinds of ducks.
The duck in the story is a mallard.
Mallards live mostly in Europe, North
America and Asia. You can find them
almost anywhere where there is water.
In winter many of them move south to
find warmer weather. Many Scandi-
navian birds fly to the British Isles, and
some even go as far as Africa. North
American mallards often winter in
Florida or Mexico. No one knows how
they find their way over such long
distances, though the positions of the
sun and the stars probably help to guide
them.

Up Tails All

Mallards are called 'dabbling ducks'
because they feed on the surface of the
water or by up-ending; when a duck is
dabbling you can see only its tail above
the surface. During the day, the ducks
feed while they are swimming, scooping
up small insects, larvae, frogspawn and

tadpoles, and waterweeds. At night
they go on to the land to eat leaves,
seeds, berries, nuts and worms.

When a duck dabbles in mud it uses
its tongue to suck the water into its bill
and then push it out again. As the muddy
water swishes out, bits of food stick to
special plates inside the bill. The duck
then swallows the food.

Not all ducks are dabblers like the
mallard; some, such as the goldeneye
and the tufted duck, dive deep down for
their food and can swim underwater.
The teal is a dabbling duck.

Fine Feathers

From September to June the drake
(male) is more brightly coloured than
the duck (female). At the end of June
the drake starts to lose its bright
feathers. From July until the end of
August it is a dull brown colour, like the
female. During this time it cannot fly
because it has lost the special flight
feathers from its wings.

'false-preening'

'mock-drinking'

'grunt-whistling'

duck 'nod-swimming'

Some courtship displays

Feathers are not only important for flying, they also keep the duck warm and dry. So it is important to keep them clean. A duck does this by running its bill over its feathers to 'comb' them. During preening the duck also spreads oil over its feathers to keep them waterproof. The oil is made in the 'preen gland' near the duck's tail. This is why water runs off a duck's back.

Show-offs

Mallards form pairs in autumn but do not mate until spring. Both the duck and the drake put on special displays to attract a mate. The duck swims among the drakes with her neck stretched out and her head nodding. This 'nodding'

shows the drakes that she is looking for a mate. Then the drakes begin displays such as 'false-preening', 'grunt-whistling' and 'mock-drinking'.

False-preening is when a drake rubs its bill over the top edge of its wing to make a rattling noise. When grunt-whistling it thrusts its bill into the water and then jerks up its head, scattering drops everywhere. As it does this, it grunts.

Mock-drinking happens when two drakes meet while a duck is nearby. They both pretend to drink, to show that they do not want to fight. When the duck decides which of the drakes is to be her mate, she nods at him. He follows her and drives away other drakes.

duck

duck

duck

drake

drake

drake

Goldeneye   **Tufted duck**   **Teal**